Johnnie, Come Home

Johnnie, Come Home

By

JOSEPHINE CUNNINGTON EDWARDS

Review and Herald® Publishing Association
Washington, DC 20039-0555
Hagerstown, MD 21740

Contents

CHAPTER ONE

Pa Returns

SMOKE CURLED upward from the chimney of the log cabin which Johnnie Lee called home. It was a good cabin, better than most people's houses, for Pa had built it strong.

Down by the river was a sawmill run by Jake Turnipseed. When Pa raised his cabin, he ceiled it with smooth boards. He put sawdust between the boards and the ceiling, which helped keep the cabin warm in winter and cool in summer.

Ma cooked at the fireplace in the lean-to built onto the cabin. A big fireplace it was, and Johnnie remembered that building it was almost the last thing his Pa had done before he died. His big sisters had helped carry the stones, and Pa had laid them in mortar mixed in Ma's big iron cooking pot. His hands had been thin, and he'd had to stop and rest often. Ma begged him to let someone else build it.

"Jake Turnipseed will finish it, Owen," she said gently. "You rest till you feel better. We can wait on that fireplace, Pa."

Pa got up wearily, picked up his trowel, and put a

smooth stone in place. "You need that fireplace badly," he said. "I aim to finish it. Jake won't make it as good as I like it. He's satisfied with 'good enough.' I'm not."

Poor Pa. He had never been well a day since he came home from the Civil War before Johnnie was born. Everyone was asleep that night. Five-year-old Tennessee, named when they had lived briefly in that state, and Ella, who was seven, were both sleeping in the trundle bed. Ida, nine, was sleeping with Ma. Then the door suddenly rattled loudly. Old Shep, lying on a sack by the fireplace, jumped up and growled deep in his throat. Snow covered the ground, for it was the coldest April in Indiana for several years.

Ma got up and slipped a shawl over her flannel nightgown. The door rattled again. Ma was frightened until she saw Shep change his attitude toward the night caller. Shep pressed his nose against the crack in the door, his tail wagging happily.

Pa called, "It's me. It's Owen. I've come home."

"O Owen!" cried Ma, her voice bubbling with joy. Her trembling fingers tore at the door. "Come in, Owen —come in. It's so cold out there. I'll stir up the fire, and——"

"Ma, I'm going to take my clothes off out here in the shed," Pa said. "The army fellows all got body lice. My uniform's full of them, and I ain't goin' to bring them in. Hand me a blanket or a quilt."

Ma stepped to the big chest in the corner in an instant. "Here's a wool shirt, and some warm underpants I made ye, Owen. I wove it and made it 'gainst your comin' home."

Johnnie had heard again and again how Ma stirred up the fire, and Pa took the first good bath he'd had in years. She brought in the wooden tub Grampa had made with homemade staves. Then, with a bowlful of soft soap and a big rough home-woven towel, Pa took his bath while Ma raked the coals and cooked supper. She served him hoecake baked in the long-legged skillet, some fried meat, gravy, and a couple of sweet potatoes baked in the hot coals.

Pa said later he'd never eaten anything that tasted as good. For a long time during the war he was lucky to get enough parched corn to satisfy the gnawing in his stomach.

Long exposure to wet and cold, moldy food, and filth gave him dysentery that he never overcame. He had a bad cough that almost took his breath away at times.

Ma tried to nurse him the best she could. She mulled cider for him and made him drink it hot while he sat toasting his feet at the fireplace.

Johnnie was born about a year after Pa returned home, and Pa cut down a gnarled old cherry tree someone had planted nearly fifty years before to make Johnnie a cradle. It was a beautiful thing. Ma was proud of it. Then he began on the house. Even though he was thin and sick, Pa pushed his weary body to near exhaustion every day. It was as if he had a time limit and wanted to get his house done before it was too late.

Owen felt fairly good during the summer. Ma and the girls helped him set out young fruit trees he received from Cincinnati. All over the field west of the log house, the strong young trees, like oversized buggy whips, began to put out leaves. Owen hauled manure tirelessly to the young trees. And he hauled water, too, when the rains held off for two hot months.

But Pa died in November, when the weather turned brittle cold. He left a good house, a young orchard, and twenty acres of rich bottomland cleared of trees and stumps, besides the hundred acres of woods.

He left indomitable determination in the hearts of each of his girls—a determination to be decent, hardworking, and law-abiding. But he left little to Johnnie, who grew up a somewhat spoiled only son. Ida, Ella, and Tennessee gave him everything he wanted. Ma tried to train the fatherless child correctly, but it was uphill work after Owen died. After her daily farm chores and the housework were completed, little time remained to be the best mother.

When Johnnie was five, Ma married Si Merwin, who owned a farm but lived in town, where he operated a shoe-repair shop. He was a widower with a half-grown son and a married daughter. After marrying Ma, he moved out to the farmhouse and brought all his fine furniture with him.

Johnnie never forgot the day Si moved in, for that was the first time Ma ever had a "bureau dresser" with a mirror to look into when she wanted to fix her hair or straighten her dress. The dresser had drawers, too, to put things in.

Si also brought a good sofa bed made of light brown velvet with pictures of dark brown leaves all over it. It was placed against the log wall by the big sitting room fireplace. Ma put a large oval braided rug in front of it. Si built a partition in both the cabin and the lean-to so the girls would have their own bedroom. Si and Ma's room was shared by little Johnnie, who had now graduated to the trundle bed. Having a new father made life easier for the family, but Si gave everyone chores to do.

Ella and Tennessee washed the dishes after all meals and helped with the cleaning and washing. Johnnie kept the chip and cob buckets full and fed corn to the hens.

One day when Johnnie was eight, he decided not to gather cobs. He whined and blubbered, for it was cold outside, and he liked the fireside and playing with the amiable old tomcat on the warm hearth.

Ma was frying big fat doughnuts in a black pot on the back of the stove, and the sweet oily smell filled the whole house. As fast as Ma forked doughnuts out of the pot, Ella sprinkled them with sugar and piled them up on a blue meat platter. Johnnie's mouth watered at the thought of eating fresh doughnuts with his mug of cold milk for supper. Then Si came in from town, where he worked at his shoe shop three afternoons a week. He was happy, and the children were glad to see him. He brought home a big slab of cheese and some thick store crackers, a great treat in those days.

"Hello, everyone," he boomed, and the girls and Ma all answered him from the kitchen.

"My, things smell wonderful around here," he said heartily. But as he hung his great coat up on the peg in the wall by the fireplace, his eyes fell on the empty chip and cob buckets.

"Why, what's this?" he said sternly to Johnnie, who had neither looked up nor greeted him, but just sat still on the brick hearth.

"Where are the chips and cobs for the morning fires?" he asked. "Didn't I tell you to fill those buckets twice a day?"

Johnnie didn't look up. "It was cold outside," he said in a low voice. "I didn't want to go. Too cold."

Just then Ma called, "Supper's ready, Si. Get washed up to eat. Come while it's hot."

"Johnnie ain't eatin' any supper till he gets his cobs and chips," he answered. "Get your coat on, Johnnie, and fill them buckets. What you could have done by daylight, you'll have to do in the dark. Now, stir up your stumps and get movin' or I'll have to see to your disobedience."

One look at Si's face was enough for Johnnie, and he put on his coat, took the buckets, and scuttled out into the darkness. He would have cried and whined to Ma or Ella, but he knew Si would give him a taste of the heavy razor strop if he complained.

The meal was half over before Johnnie slipped into his place at the table next to Ella. Both buckets stood full by the kitchen door.

Si reached over and gave the lad a hearty pat on the shoulder. "Good fellow!" he said. "You're growin' up."

Driving out from town one day, Si saw Bill Hoskin going to the river with a bag. "What are you doin', Bill? Where ya goin'?"

"Goin' to the river to drown this pup. Got too many dogs around."

"Wait a minute, Bill. My boy ain't got a dog. Let me take that feller home to him."

"Well, take him if you want to, but he surely ain't much to look at."

When Si got home that night, he was still carrying the little dog in the sack. He brought him into the kitchen and handed the sack to Johnnie.

Feist tumbled out of the sack, fearful and trembling. He sank down to the floor, his wobbly legs unable to hold his quivering body. Johnnie got an old tin pan, poured fresh milk in it, crumbled up some of Ma's homemade bread into it, and dragged the little dog up to the pan.

Poor little Feist hadn't eaten for some days. His little sides were caved in, and his ribs were showing. He crept cringingly to the pan and put almost his whole little yellow face in the warm milk, his tail between his legs. The pan was emptied in only a minute or two.

Johnnie made Feist a bed in a wooden tub that leaked water and was no good for washing. He laid a flour sack and a ragged coat in the tub and put the dog in it. Johnnie stayed by him, petting and talking to the pup until he quieted down and went to sleep.

Later, when the weather was warm, Ma let Johnnie sleep in the barn like other farm boys did. After that, he and Feist were inseparable, and they loved each other dearly. They were together, working, roaming the woods, trudging the dusty roads all day, and sleeping on a home-woven blanket in the hay side by side at night. Feist quickly learned Johnnie's vocabulary. If Johnnie said, "Rats," Feist knew he must run to the tunnels that the destructive gray pests made under the house and the granary. And between them, a rat, or two, or half a dozen, would be killed and laid out on the ground. Feist seized them by the neck and threw them into the air. When they came down, their backs broken, a few vicious shakes quickly killed them.

The man who owned the mill in town was rich. At least, the neighbors thought he was. Mrs. Moore had a carpet on her parlor floor, and stuffed furniture she called a parlor "suite." A melodeon stood at one side, which the Moores' daughter, Agnes, played delicately, having learned to play in Boston, where she had gone to school for a year. A melodeon is similar to a pump organ, only smaller.

The Moores ate in the dining room every day. Once when Ella "worked out" for Mrs. Moore, she told Ma that Mrs. Moore didn't like for Mr. Moore to come to the dining table wearing his old mill clothes.

Si and the girls laughed uproariously at that, but Ma said, "I don't think it's a bit nice for you to come in from cleanin' out the stable to eat. It almost turns a body's stomach."

Si sobered at Ma's serious face. "She's right, children," he said. "We can take a little pains bein' clean when we come in to eat. It's only respect." That was one thing about Si that Johnnie always liked. He took up for the mother in front of the children.

The townspeople liked Mr. and Mrs. Moore, but even the old grandmas shook their heads at the way they were spoiling their son Greg. He had everything he ever desired, and more besides. And he never had to

work. He became a real bully, but of course his parents
did not recognize it.

"I reckon the reason they are so lavish with Greg is
they had bad luck with their other children," Ma commented one day when the subject of Greg and his mean-
ness came up. It was true. They'd had a pair of twin
boys and a daughter, all of them older than Greg. When
typhoid fever went through the country like wildfire, all
three of the Moore children died and were buried
in one week.

"I tell you, I thought Mrs. Moore would lose her
mind, the way she carried on. No wonder she sets such
store by that boy Greg," Ma said.

But even so, Johnnie didn't like him. Greg had a
following, though, because he had a gun, a horse, and
usually a little money in his pocket. He had a vicious,
quarrelsome bulldog that the boys in the neighborhood
hated almost as much as they hated him.

Johnnie couldn't understand why Greg thought so
much of his mean dog, and looked with more favor on
his little Feist. Indeed, the wriggling, fawning creature
had almost human wisdom.

Feist would sit for minutes and watch Johnnie with
unblinking eyes. Johnnie would say, "Feist, go fetch my
boots," and the little yellow animal would spring into
action. If he'd say, "Feist, go get the cows," away the
little dog ran to the pasture, his feet hardly touching
the ground. Johnnie knew the cows would be at the
pasture gate. Feist, watchful and alert, raced along behind the cows, driving them home.

When Johnnie milked, he aimed a stream of milk

straight for Feist's mouth, and the dog swallowed it excitedly.

Feist was useful in other ways, too. He could tree a coon or flush a rabbit or partridge out faster than Greg Moore's fancy bulldog ever dreamed of doing, and that didn't make Greg very happy or friendly.

Greg always made fun of Feist. Of course, this made Johnnie feel bad, for he thought his dog was amazingly smart and even beautiful. He told himself that Greg was jealous because Feist ran faster than the other dogs when the boys went hunting.

One night, when Johnnie was almost twelve, the neighborhood boys went on a coon hunt. Greg took Bo, his ugly bulldog, along, and Johnnie took Feist. Johnnie was watchful of Bo and Greg, for Bo had killed several dogs and was mean and dangerous. People claimed that Greg sicced him on other dogs, and Johnnie did not doubt it.

Greg had Bo on a leash, but Feist was bouncing ahead, barking joyously. Suddenly a rabbit darted out, and he chased after it. Greg loosed Bo.

"Sic him, Bo," the boy whispered tensely. "Get old Feist."

Johnnie heard the hateful whisper.

Bo snarled and leaped ahead. The rabbit shied to one side, and Feist, taken unaware, darted on ahead. So did Bo.

Cal Stermer seized Johnnie's arm so hard that the nails bit into the flesh. "Did you hear Greg, Johnnie? That bulldog's gonna kill Feist. I heard him!"

"I heard, too," hissed Johnnie, breaking into a full

run. All the boys were running now to keep up with the dogs.

Bo overtook Feist and with one slash laid his shoulder open to the bone.

Feist gave a shrill cry of pain; then, quick as lightning, the little rough-haired Feist turned on the big lubberly dog, seizing a huge front paw in his sharp, razorlike teeth.

Bo, unnerved by the unexpected turn of events, fell backward with a cry of terror.

Greg leaped forward, almost insane with fury. "Kill him! Kill that Feist!" he shrieked. "He's killing Bo. He'll cripple him for life. He attacked Bo!"

In his rage, he picked up a club and would have struck Feist if the boys had not stopped him.

"No, you don't, Greg," one boy said roughly. "You sicced him on Feist. We heard you."

"Yeah. You're always pesterin' and makin' fun of Johnnie. You got what's coming to you," another added.

But meanwhile Feist grimly chewed on.

Johnnie stood watching a moment. Then he strode forward. "Let be, Feist," he commanded. "Let's go home."

Instantly the little dog obeyed, and Johnnie and Feist turned and left the group. Little Feist bounded ahead excitedly.

CHAPTER TWO

The Gun Accident

JOHNNIE KNEW little about God, for his parents seldom went inside a church. There was an old Bible at home which Pa's mother had brought by covered wagon from North Carolina. But Pa, who had not been able to go to school, was unable to read a word. Neither could Ma, so no one opened the big book.

Johnnie could barely read because he had not gone very far in school. He had pneumonia so much that the neighbors said that Ma would never raise him.

When Johnnie was fourteen, Ma and Si became interested in religion. A revival was held at the New Light Christian Church by six preachers who had come down from Indianapolis. The meetings offered excitement and music, and the whole neighborhood, hungry for a place to go, turned out. The doctrine of an eternally burning hell was so vividly described that some people fainted.

Si, Ma, Ella, and Tennessee joined the church. But not Johnnie. He was neither scared nor convicted. The idea of a revengeful, angry God did not stir him at all.

"I wouldn't even holler," he told himself. "A big

feller like God pickin' on folks like my Pa, who never had learning enough to read and join the church. Why, Pa never stole or lied; and if he killed, it was in the war, and he didn't want to do it. Pa worked like a slave so we could have a good house. Would God destroy him because he didn't know enough to join a church? I can't follow a God like that."

Si and Ma had a pretty baby girl whom Johnnie loved and delighted to carry around. She loved him, too, and would watch the door and squeal with delight when he opened it. Ma said she believed if she could, she would jump right out of her cradle and run to him when Johnnie came into the room.

Little Margie died of croup at eleven months, and Johnnie almost died of grief. He became ill and ran a high fever, and the neighbors said the grass would not be green on Margie's grave until there would be another grave beside hers. But he got well. Because of what was said at Margie's funeral, Johnnie felt he had another count against God. He almost raged out loud when one of the preachers said in a sonorous voice: "Inasmuch as it hath pleased God to wound us. . . ."

"Pleased God!" Johnnie stormed inwardly, hot tears spilling down his cheeks at the sight of the white casket holding his little half sister. "To think it *pleased* God to see little Margie fairly choke to death! Oh, I hate Him —I hate Him—I do—I do, I do!"

Later that winter Johnnie got pneumonia again, and this time he came the closest to death. Two preachers came at Ma and Si's request to pray for him. Johnnie bitterly turned his face to the wall.

"Johnnie, make your peace with God; please do," Ma pleaded. "Johnnie, dear, do you hear me? I'm afraid you ain't going to live, Johnnie. You ain't ready to go."

"No. No, no, Ma! I ain't never done anything to God. Why should I make peace with Him when I ain't harmed Him none? I don't even like God, Ma. He took little Margie, and I ain't never done no harm."

An angry, vengeful God, ruthless and unpitying, was all he knew; and his young heart was full of hate for and fear of such a God.

Because Pa had been a soldier, Johnnie was interested in guns and swords of all kinds. When he was eight, he found a rag and polished Pa's gun until it shone. Then, because he knew Ma would not let him play with it if she knew, he sneaked it out of the house.

"Could be I could kill a bear, or even a fox," he thought. "Wouldn't Ma be surprised and pleased? I could tan that bearskin and lay it by my bed; then when I got out of bed in the wintertime, it would feel right warm to my feet, it would."

He had walked far into the woods by that time with the heavy gun. He didn't see a bear, or a deer, or even a partridge. Then he began to wonder if the gun was loaded. He didn't know how to load or unload a gun; he only knew that to shoot, you pull the trigger. Tired of carrying the heavy firearm, he stopped and took it off his shoulder. He tried to do it nonchalantly as he had seen others do who had been used to handling guns. But as the gun slid through his small hands, he touched the trigger.

"*Bang!*"

The air seemed to split wide open with sound. A fiery zigzag of pain, white-hot and terrible, tore up from his foot, and Johnnie screamed. The bullet had cut off his third toe at the first joint.

Now what would Ma say? She would hate to see his foot torn up like that. Most likely she would tan his britches. He knew Ma, and he knew she had told him again and again to let the gun alone, not to touch it for any reason. The pain was great, but he hobbled home. Ma was in the kitchen, so he returned the gun to its place by the chimney corner without her seeing him.

When he heard the dinner gong clanging to call Si in from the field, he knew he would have to eat, whether he felt like it or not. He crept into the kitchen, pain throbbing through his foot every step he took. Who would have thought that the end of a toe was so important or that losing it would hurt so?

Ma was busy and paid no attention to Johnnie as he came into the kitchen. She had opened the oven door, pulled out a skillet full of crusty corn bread, and set it down on the hearth. Ella, his older sister, cut the bread into wedges and piled it up on a round bread plate.

By the time Tennessee and Si reached the table, the room whirled round and round, it seemed to Johnnie. Ella, turning in her chair, accidentally kicked Johnnie's foot, and he uttered a loud, wailing cry, and then the room went black.

Voices seemed far away when Johnnie came to. He heard Ma say, "How in the world do you suppose Johnnie hurt his foot? Why, his toe is half gone!"

He could not hear what Ella replied, or Si either,

for someone poured more water on his face, nearly drowning him.

The pain came in heavy throbs when he was finally able to sit up in a chair. Ma, usually spunky and hard as tacks, was gentle and tender in her talk. He was surprised that she did not threaten to punish him when she heard he had been playing with the gun. She only told him not to play with it again, and he fervently promised he wouldn't.

"I put a bread-and-milk poultice on your foot to draw out the fever, Johnnie," she said. "Now, maybe this will be a lesson to you."

Johnnie was sitting in the old rocker. She brought him a plate of dinner, and as he looked at it, his foot taken care of, his hunger returned. He ate a chunk of yellow corn bread that was fairly slathered in butter. Turnip greens, a big sweet potato, and a cup of sorghum for his corn bread rounded out his meal.

Ma and Si often urged Johnnie to go to church. But he never would, unless it was just for an evening, and he stayed at the back so that he could go out when he wanted to. He seemed to find more pleasure in being with young men who played cards, drank beer, and smoked cigars and pipes than with those who went to church. Soon Johnnie himself drank and smoked. He had been drunk many times before he was sixteen.

One day in town Johnnie bought a big turkey gobbler from a man who had won it at a raffle and wanted to sell it.

"This will please Ma," he thought. "She has a hen turkey, and she has always wanted to raise little turkeys."

The big fowl weighed more than twenty pounds, and Johnnie proudly drove his buggy into the barnyard with the turkey in a big crate beside him. Ma came out of the hen house with her apron filled with eggs.

"Ma, Ma!" he called, throwing the lines over the dashboard and jumping out. "I've got a present for you!"

Ma carefully put the eggs from her apron into a basket. Then she shook out her apron and came up to the buggy as Johnnie pulled the big crate out.

"Johnnie, where in the world did you get that big turkey?" she asked. "Why, he's a beauty, the prettiest turkey I ever saw!"

"I got him from Jim Cotney, Ma," he answered proudly. "He won him at a raffle, but he wanted a drink worse than he wanted a turkey, so he sold him to me cheap. He's yours, Ma. Want me to let him out here?"

"No, Johnnie. Let's fasten him in the chicken run until he gets used to the place. My, but I surely do thank you, Johnnie. He's a wonderful present. You're a good boy, Johnnie."

He let the big turkey out, and together they watched him strut and walk to and fro. He at once made himself at home, just as if he had always lived there.

"Can we roast him for Thanksgiving dinner, Ma?" asked Ella, watching the great fellow strut about.

"I should say not," Ma replied. "We have ducks and chickens aplenty, but we would have to go far to find another turkey like that. I want to raise little turkeys so that when another Thanksgiving comes, I can sell lots of them. Maybe in another year we can think of turkey and bog cranberries, but not now."

Johnnie bought a gun of his own, and he kept it with him most of the time. He shot weasels that pestered the chickens, and he kept rabbits out of Si's new orchard.

That winter Johnnie was ill an unusually long time. Ma kept him plastered with onion poultices, for she thought there was nothing better for fighting a cold, pneumonia, or pleurisy.

Johnnie hated the smell of onion and wished he could get a bath or go swimming. But he knew Ma would never listen to such an idea. Folks thought a bath might kill a person who had been as sick as Johnnie had been. Ma made him sit so close to the fireplace that the flannel soaked in onions, goose grease, and mustard made him itch miserably. Ma and the girls were at a quilting bee, and Johnnie became restless.

The snow was almost gone. The grass was turning green in the yard. Ma had let the hens and the turkeys out to scratch for themselves that late March day. Johnnie parted Ma's snowy curtains and looked outside.

He pulled his cap down on his long straggling hair. Then he struggled into his old barn coat, carefully buttoning it up to his chin.

"A little air ain't going to hurt me," he thought. Weakly he walked around the yard, and then opened the little gate that led into the barnyard. There lay the woodpile. Johnnie had not split any wood for almost two months.

Seeing an old pepper can lying on the trash pile, he picked it up, set it on the top of the woodpile on a stick of wood, then got his gun from the house.

He leaned against the gate and aimed, barely seeing the little brown spot on the can he knew as a picture of a lion's head. Ma always got Lion-brand pepper.

Then he shot. When he went over to look, he saw he had missed the pepper can entirely.

"Could be my hand shook so it spoiled my aim," he muttered. "I better get into practice."

He shot several times but didn't hit the little can. The last time he shot, he heard the hens and roosters on the other side of the woodpile make a terrible noise.

He slowly reloaded his gun, thinking nothing of the chickens until he heard his mother's voice.

"Johnnie, *what* are you doin' out here? What have you done?"

Looking up, he saw Ella coming around the woodpile carrying the big tom turkey. That last bullet had gone through the woodpile somehow and had hit the proud old gobbler in his bright red wattled throat.

"Johnnie, I wouldn't a had you done that for a ten-dollar gold piece. Now with spring comin', where can I get me a good gobbler?"

They had roast turkey, sliced turkey, and turkey giblets for a whole week. Tennessee, Ella, and Johnnie said they never wanted to look at a turkey again.

The next day Johnnie felt well enough to hitch up the horse and drive ten miles to Windfall. He'd heard a farmer near there had turkeys to sell. It took him all day to go and return. It also took all the money he had saved. But he brought back a handsome tom turkey.

The next turkey was almost as big as the old one, and Ma was satisfied.

"This time, you stay away from my turkeys with your gun," she warned the boy, laughing.

While he was gone, she had made half a dozen rhubarb pies. They were cooling on top of the kitchen "safe"—a cupboard with punched tin doors. The crusts were delicately brown, and some of the rosy juice had bubbled out and covered parts of the upper crusts with waxy sweetness.

"Ma," Johnnie said, haltingly, as he looked at the pies.

"What is it, Johnnie?" Ma looked up from the dishpan where she was scrubbing the stained piepans.

"I've always wanted a pie—in a round piece," he answered, looking at his mother out of the corner of his eye.

The stern look died out of Ma's eyes for a minute. All she saw was the pleading face of her thin, gangling son.

"Could be it'd be good for you," she conceded. "Granny Lee always said rhubarb cleared the phlegm out of a body. Take one, and welcome, Johnnie. You're so thin you look like the runnin' gears of a cricket."

Johnnie picked up a big warm pie and sat on a stool before the fireplace. He slipped off his gum boots, stretching his toes in his thick yarn socks. Then he began eating his pie, the first time in his life he had ever eaten a whole pie at one sitting.

Ma set a long-legged skillet of pone to bake over the coals raked onto the brick hearth. Even though she had a high-oven Monarch stove, she always said no cookstove could bake pone like a fireplace. So she did some of her cooking at the fireplace as long as she lived.

"You'll spoil your supper, eating that whole pie, Johnnie," she said.

"O Ma, no I won't," he answered laughingly. "It'll just barely take off the edge of my hunger."

She had potato soup, flavored with onions and rich milk that was half cream. Poured over pone, it made a rich and hearty meal. Johnnie ate two big bowls of it, besides a lot of apple butter spread thick on the crusty corn pone.

"Don't reckon you'll want any pie," Ma remarked, cutting the big pastries in quarters.

"Why, yes," answered Johnnie guilelessly. "Yes, I could do with a piece of pie, Ma." They all laughed.

"Johnnie, I do declare," said his mother, "both your legs must be hollow for sure!"

After supper, Ella and Ida were obviously preparing to go out.

"Where you goin'?" Johnnie asked. They had hurried through the dishes so that they could pretty themselves up in their new flowered challis dresses.

"To Wade Burke's," answered Ella happily. "Myrtie Burke is having a party. They asked everyone in the neighborhood to come. Ma said the night air might make *you* sick. You can't go. Myrtie said they was goin' to have hickory-nut candy."

Johnnie sat thinking. There weren't any nut trees growing in Burkes' woods. He knew where those nuts came from. The fall before, Johnnie had gone to the woods and gathered three big bags of hickory nuts. He dragged them to the fence, then went home and hitched the horse to the spring wagon to bring the bags home.

When he returned with the wagon, all three bags were gone. He hated to lose the bags worse than the nuts. He didn't know who had taken them, but he had an idea. He drove down the road and saw Clem Middleton chopping wood in his barn lot.

"Seen anyone go past here in the last half hour?" he asked the old man.

"Nope," answered Clem. "No one but Wade Burke, drivin' like Jehu. Oughta be a law agin sich reckless drivin'. Gonna hurt somebody someday."

Johnnie pretended to go to bed early after the girls left for the party. He waited till he heard Ma and Si lock the house, wind the clock, and go to their room. Then Johnnie sneaked out, bundled up in his woolen coat. It wasn't far to Burkes' farm. It was just beyond Middletons'. Johnnie walked across the lots and headed for the corncrib, back by the barn. Opening the door cautiously, he saw his three bags of nuts sitting in the bright moonlight. Another bag was there, too, filled with black walnuts. One of the bags of hickory nuts was more than half empty. He knew his bags. Si had painted a red streak on each of them.

It didn't take Johnnie long to drag his hickory-nut bags into the barnyard, heave them into the spring wagon the girls came in, and put them under the seat. Ella and Ida wouldn't pay any attention to what was in the wagon when they went home. Next day he'd put them in the barn.

Johnnie returned home, careful to take a cob and clean his boots before he went into the house. Ma didn't hear him come in, for she was snoring when he sneaked past her room and up the stairs.

Next morning at breakfast the girls were talking about the party. "We ate all the fudge," Ella said, "and Mrs. Burke sent Wade out to get more nuts so the younger children could crack them while we played some games."

"Yes, sir," Ida broke in excitedly, "Wade came in mad as hops. Every single bag of his hickory nuts had been taken while we were playing."

"I was so mad at Wade I could have died," Ella said angrily. "He came straight over to Ida and me and said in his hateful voice, 'Where did you say Johnnie was tonight, Ella?' "

"Yes, and Ella spoke right up and told Wade you'd been sick with pneumonia and weren't able to go to parties yet."

"No, Johnnie went to bed before I did," said Ma, bringing a big platter of hot pancakes from the stove. "He never left this house. If he had, I would have known it."

But Johnnie kept still. He didn't realize it was wrong to act a lie. All he knew was that now he had his own hickory nuts and no others. He knew they were his because of the big dab of red Si had painted on each sack.

CHAPTER THREE

Pig in the Garden

Si, THE KIND STEPFATHER, died. Ma was a widow again.

Johnnie was much taller, but he did not do any better in his classes at the district school. If there had been kind, understanding teachers, things might have been different. He had a cold almost constantly because of his poor diet at home. Ma tried to "fill her children up," but she knew nothing about vitamins, minerals, or roughage. The family had barrels of salt pork, and sausage preserved in crocks in beds of melted lard. Vinegar, homemade mustard, cabbage boiled pink, white bread, black coffee, and strong tea were thought to be a good diet for everyone, children and adults alike. No one knew why Chrissie, his cousin, got rheumatism and remained in bed until fresh fruit and vegetables came into season.

Because Johnnie didn't do well in his lessons, he often played tricks on people. One day he stayed home to shuck corn. He had to go to the neighbors' to borrow some tool, and he went by the schoolhouse. He saw a big two-by-four piece of lumber lying in the yard. Leaping over the fence and giggling to himself, he put the long stick through a hole in the foundation of the building. Then using the edge of the foundation for a base, he pried up and beat the floor of the schoolroom hard. Boom! Boom! Boom!

He knew Mr. Marcus, the schoolmaster, would come out in a hurry and find him if he didn't run. Quickly shoving the long piece of lumber under the building, he darted behind a clump of bushes.

Sure enough, the door burst open and Mr. Marcus came striding out, furious. He whirled around the schoolhouse like the wind, sure he'd catch the culprit who disturbed his classes. He even looked under the building, but he couldn't see a thing in the darkness. Johnnie lay behind a bush and watched him gleefully.

Chuckling to himself, the boy went down the creek bed to the neighbors' and didn't let himself be seen by anyone. He was pleased that he had gotten something on old Marcus. He almost hated the schoolmaster. That was one reason he detested school.

One day Mr. Marcus told the boys to stay away from the irrigation ditch that flowed past the schoolyard. The days were becoming warmer, and the teacher knew the boys would be tempted to go swimming.

"If I catch one of you in the ditch, you'll get a taste of the hickory stick," he threatened darkly.

Mr. Marcus often rode home horseback for a hot dinner, since he lived only a quarter of a mile away. One day several boys were waiting for just this. The day had been unseasonably hot, and their long winter underclothes made them itch mercilessly. A swim in the ditch would put new life into them, and Mr. Marcus needn't know a thing about it.

Johnnie didn't go, but sat under a tree and ate his lunch. He still didn't feel well from his bout with pneumonia. Soon the boys came sneaking back, rubbing their heads frantically so that their hair would be dry before the schoolmaster returned. Greg Moore filled his cap with water, and sneaking up behind Johnnie, emptied it on his head.

"Greg!" shouted several of the boys. "Don't you know Johnnie's been sick?"

"Yeah, playin' off sick, so he could get out of work," jeered Greg, laughing in Johnnie's face. In a minute the schoolmaster came riding into the schoolyard, angry as a nest of hornets.

"Any you boys been in that ditch water?" he demanded. "Sophie Strom says you were."

He strode up to Johnnie and felt his hair. "Yeah! You! You been in that ditch!"

Johnnie started to get up and open his mouth to deny it, but the angry schoolmaster dealt him such a blow across the side of the head that the boy fell backward, hitting his head against the root of an elm tree.

While Johnnie was trying to get up again, both hands up to his splitting head, the other boys ran up to the teacher shouting, "Johnnie didn't go in, Mr. Marcus! He didn't! He didn't!"

"How come his hair is all wet then?" he demanded. "You're lying to save him!"

"We ain't lyin', Mr. Marcus," shouted Len Jones, his face red with fury. "Greg poured water on his head, and you're gonna kill Johnnie, hittin' him on the head like that. Don't you know he's been awful sick?"

After that, Johnnie hated Mr. Marcus, and going to school was in vain, for the cold fury he felt every time he saw the lean, dried-up little man kept him from learning.

He often played hooky, but old Marcus never said a word about Johnnie's absence after he had beaten Johnnie that day for something he hadn't done. And Johnnie felt even more hate in his heart for Greg Moore for causing him to be thrashed.

Greg had a pig he was fattening up to sell. He used to brag about all the things he was going to do with his "hog money," and had it spent, in his plans, twenty different ways. Since Moores' hog lot was near Johnnie's house, he saw that much-bragged-about hog all the time. Then the young porker began to periodically get through his fence and into Ma's garden. She chased him out several times, sputtering and scolding at the damage the greedy pig had done. But she didn't do anything about it, for Ma was one for living at peace with her neighbors.

"That pig of Moore's rooted up half a row of my young turnips," she told Johnnie one day. "Go fix the fence."

When Johnnie went to fix it, there was the fat porker in the turnips again. It squealed every step to the fence, and Johnnie almost wished he could do something to it, to get revenge on Greg. But he drove it through the hole in the fence with an extra hard kick with his boot on its curly tail.

There had been a stray dog, half wild, doing a lot of damage among the sheep. A few nights earlier, it had prowled near the rubbish pails by the summer kitchen porch, and Johnnie determined to get him. He kept his rifle on one of the old tables in the summer kitchen so that it would be handy.

One night Ma and the girls went to a meeting the Methodists were having at the schoolhouse. Since Johnnie didn't want to go, he lounged around home, smoking an old pipe and watching the flames in the fireplace. Soon he heard a noise. He leaped up.

"It's that dog," he muttered. "I'm going to get him."

In a few minutes he was on the dark porch, his rifle cocked. A black shape moved near the rubbish buckets. Carefully he took aim, leaning his gun against the doorjamb to steady himself. Then he fired. He saw the shape crumple to the ground, then lie still.

He lit the lantern and crept outside to see if the dog was dead. He took a stick of cordwood with him to finish the job if it wasn't. A wounded, wild dog can be a dangerous animal.

Imagine Johnnie's surprise when he saw the creature he had killed was—the pig Greg Moore was always bragging about. Now he was in a quandary. Ma would think she'd have to pay for the pig to keep peace with the neighbors, and Johnnie didn't think she ought to, for the pig had spoiled half her turnip patch and rooted up two or three young peach trees.

After some thought, he loaded the dead pig into the wheelbarrow, took it a short distance down the road, and dumped it in a deep culvert by the bridge. Then he came back, cleaned out the wheelbarrow, and went to bed. He was fast asleep when Ma and the girls came home.

Next morning, Ma told him at breakfast she thought that old dog had been around, because all the rubbish pails had been turned over.

He snickered to himself when Ella said angrily, "Greg was over here looking for his pig, Ma. Said it disappeared. Asked where Johnnie was last night."

"I hope you told him," Ma said crossly, "that Johnnie was at home and in bed. And if he gets too smart about that pig, show him our orchard and the turnip patch."

"I did, Ma," answered Ella. "I told him you was pretty mad about what that pig has been doing, but we don't know where it is."

"I hope that settled him," remarked Ida.

But Johnnie kept his eyes on the food on his plate and didn't say a word.

CHAPTER FOUR

The Bear

SOMETHING was bothering Ma's chickens. Johnnie heard her complain three mornings in a row at the breakfast table.

"My, but the chickens set up an uproar last night," she said, splitting open a hot biscuit. "Pass me the apple butter, Johnnie. Something's going to get in and kill them one of these days."

"What do you think it is, Ma?" Johnnie asked. "A coon, a fox, or maybe a weasel?"

"I don't know, Johnnie," she answered, getting up and pouring a little boiling water into the coffee pot. "Could be any of them. When I was a little shaver, a bear got into our hen house. Scratches on the chicken house are real high up."

"Some people say there are bears in Hawkins' big stretch of woods," remarked Ida. "Jed Merom says he's seen one, anyway."

"Can't depend on nothin' Jed says," remarked Johnnie. "He'd tell you he saw an elephant, if he was drunk enough."

"You drink yourself, and you know you do," accused Ella. "Bill Jarret told me you was drunker than a lord last Saturday night at Pipers' barn dance."

Johnnie said nothing. He felt mad at Ella for blurting out things like that.

No one spoke for a moment. Johnnie was a little ashamed, knowing that Ma had heard about his getting drunk, and he felt like wringing Ella's neck for mentioning it. But he had no idea Pipers' cider was that hard, and the fellows had kept urging him on. He'd been sick afterward and had slept in the Pipers' haymow till nearly morning. But when Ma heard bad things about him, a light seemed to go out of her eyes, like someone had snuffed out candles, leaving only darkness.

Suddenly he wasn't hungry anymore. He jumped up so quickly that his chair fell over backward. Going outside, he got his gun from the summer kitchen and headed for the woods. He rode his horse about five miles into the back country before he came to the outer reaches of Hawkins' woods. There were no posted signs, for Hawkins had died, and his heirs didn't seem to care who hunted there, or when, or how often.

Johnnie had put a piece of cold corn bread in his pocket before he left the house, thinking it might satisfy his hunger in case he didn't get back for dinner. There were about four hundred acres of woods, and he had gotten lost there a time or two. He hobbled old Belle and let her graze while he entered the dense woods on foot.

He hadn't walked long till he stopped, took a piece of pigtail tobacco out of his pocket, and bit off a "chaw." Then, while he hunted, moving bushes, walking around trees, his jaws worked rhythmically, turning his saliva grasshopper-juice brown. He shifted the great wet quid from cheek to cheek, the liquid making his teeth slowly change to a nasty tan.

Johnnie strode through the woods, chewing his tobacco, but going as quietly as possible. Once he came to a little rise of ground, and a stream of water, crystal clear, trickled out of the side of the hill. He took out his quid and drank long and deeply of the delicious cold spring water. He saw many rabbits, but he was in no mood for rabbit today.

He wanted to find the "varmint" that had been bothering Ma's chickens.

Before noon he came to a little stream so narrow that long grass trailed in it on either side. As the weather was very warm, Johnnie took off his heavy shoes and socks and waded in the edge of the stream for a while, then ate his corn bread slowly.

He rounded some thick brush and climbed a small hill. Long ago he had learned to walk as silently as an Indian. Not a twig crackled, and Johnnie stood by a great oak tree. Then he saw a lovely sight. Across a deep-gashed ravine, where water flowed when the rains were heavy in the early spring, was a bear. In fact, three bears—a mother with two cubs.

Where had they come from? No one had seen a bear in that region for at least ten years. Ma had said that in her girlhood, before the Civil War, bears came close and ate with the hogs and cattle sometimes. And green corn was never safe from their marauding. They liked roasting ears as well as people did.

Johnnie watched the baby bears walk away a little distance and sit, their beady, mischievous eyes on their mother. Then they'd rush her and tumble her. Her great paws would flail out in every direction. She seemed to be enjoying the fun as much as her babies.

He hated to spoil such a pretty scene. He raised his gun several times, only to lower it in reluctance. But he knew a mother bear could be exceedingly dangerous and could kill a child in a moment if she were hindered or cornered. He knew she'd have to rob for her food, since the country was built up. That, in itself, constituted danger.

When he at last took careful aim and shot her in the head, the mother stood for a long moment, as if stunned, then fell where she stood. When the smoke cleared, the cubs were both gone. Johnnie thought they'd run into the cave for safety.

He hurried home and asked one of his friends to help him take the old bear back on a sled. They couldn't find the cubs. Later a man ten miles away caught one of them and tried to tame him. But the little fellow remained surly and dangerous. He refused to eat and literally starved himself to death.

Johnnie skinned the mother bear's great fat carcass. Ma knew how to tan animal hides, so they worked the big skin until it was as soft as glove leather. Ma rendered out the fat until she had several big jugs of bear oil. It was then thought to be a remedy for colds, pneumonia, and croup, if rubbed blisteringly hot on the chest and neck.

Johnnie used it, too, on his big heavy boots to make

them soft and waterproof. They had bear oil to use for a long time. But when it was gone, they couldn't get any more. Johnnie must have shot the last bear that ever came into the country. The warm hide lay in front of his bed. It felt good to jump out onto on winter mornings.

"I told you those scratches on the hen house looked like bear's clawings," Ma reminded them.

CHAPTER FIVE

Jed's Chickens

OLD MAN MEROM was a bachelor, and was Wade Burke's uncle. He lived in a two-room house just beyond Burke's farm, raising Wyandotte chickens for a living. He took great pride in his fat hens and sleek roosters, and people came for miles around to buy settings of eggs and chickens from him at fancy prices. He raised wheat, oats, and corn, mainly for chicken feed, and had a good vegetable garden.

Everyone knew Merom was an infidel. He cursed so loudly and so often that women wouldn't take their children with them when they went to buy hens or eggs. "Just makes my blood run cold to hear him use God's name like that," some of the women would say.

But Jed Merom didn't care what anyone said or thought. He'd just laugh and curse more. Johnnie began to think of himself as an infidel, too. It made him feel adult and important. So he began to curse just like old Jed. He couldn't learn arithmetic or English, but he could "cuss." He made fun of people who were "bookish," and called them "lazy lubbers," afraid to dirty their hands at a real man's work.

Jed Merom was clever—clever enough to use Johnnie to his own advantage. He so wound Johnnie around his finger that he ran errands for the old villain, and even hoed in his garden for him. Sometimes Johnnie almost hated the old fellow, but was attracted to him just the same.

Ma didn't like Johnnie's friendship with Jed, and she scolded Johnnie about it often. "You're wasting your time and letting your work go to the dogs," she told him. "He's the trashiest one of the whole Burke family. Why, Johnnie, they're all ashamed of him! Livin' in that old shack, and folks say he hasn't cleaned it up for years!"

Johnnie didn't say anything, for he knew it was all true. He tried to stay away from the wily old sinner. But Jed didn't like that. He wanted to have Johnnie around working for him. One day he sent word to Johnnie to round up four or five other young men to share a keg of beer.

Johnnie was flattered to think that he was summoned to a "beer drink," so he asked three other boys, and they went down to Jed's that evening.

It was warm, and Jed had the keg in the yard. An assortment of cracked coffee cups stood on a dirty, rickety table. Jed had already sampled the beer far too much and was becoming loose-tongued and silly. Spittle ran from both sides of his mouth.

"C'mon, boys," he said, plunging his mouth down into a full cup. "Plenty—plenty for everyone!" He lifted his head and looked bleary-eyed around at the boys. "Drink, drink," he mouthed foolishly.

Johnnie hardly touched a drop. After a while, Jed looked up and commanded, "Johnnie, go get a chicken. Get a fryer. Sneak one out of Jed Swing's hen house. He won't miss it. Fried chicken will taste good with beer. I'll get the skillet and the lard." He stumbled into his dirty house.

As Johnnie walked away from the shack, he heard Jed shaking his rusty cookstove grates. "I ain't going to steal a chicken at Swing's," he suddenly told himself. "I'll get one of *Jed's*, though!"

Reaching this decision, he climbed the rail fence and circled back to Merom's own hen yard. He took pains to kill and clean the fowl of feathers before he got back to the shack. He didn't want Jed to recognize one of his own hens.

The old man took the chicken and began to cut it up for the sizzling iron skillet. "Get it at Jed's?" he asked.

"Yes, I did," answered Johnnie, anger welling up in his heart. "At Jed's."

They all sat around and ate chicken.

"Boy, this is the best chicken I ever ate," chuckled old Jed. "Thanks to Jed Swing. Keep it to yourself, boys, where we got our treat. He wouldn't like it."

The next morning when Jed went out to feed his hens, he saw feathers everywhere. He stood and thought for a long time.

"Why—why—the dirty whelp!" he shouted and began to curse Johnnie with everything he could lay his tongue to. Blind with rage, he saddled his mare and rode to the sheriff's office and lodged a complaint against Johnnie for raiding his hen roost.

"I tell you, that feller stole one of my chickens last night," he shouted.

"Johnnie?" queried the sheriff, shoving back his hat and scratching his head. "Why, that don't sound like any of the *Lees*. They're honest and respectable."

"Not Johnnie. Not him. He took it. I *know* he did, and I want you to arrest him. He ought to go to jail for this."

"Why, he will, if he stole one of your hens. But how do you know he took it? Did you see him?"

"No, I—well—I, y'see, he brung back a chicken, and we ate it, but I had no idea it was one of mine."

An amused look crept into the sheriff's eyes.

"And you sat there and helped eat it?" he asked shrewdly.

"Why, yes, but I had no idea——"

"Did he tell you where he got it?"

"He said Jed's, and I thought he meant Jed Swing's."

"Who suggested his going and getting a chicken, Jed?"

Things were becoming uncomfortable for the old man, especially since he began to see that the wind was not exactly blowing his way.

"Oh, forget it, forget it," he mumbled impatiently.

"Jed Swing might have something to say if he knew that you'd sent Johnnie to steal one of his hens. You made a mistake there. Don't you know Jed Swing is Johnnie's uncle? That was a bad break, Jed."

Jed started for the door, and the last time the sheriff saw him, he was riding his horse down the road.

CHAPTER SIX

The Visiting Preacher

JOHNNIE WAS almost twenty-one in 1897. Because of pneumonia, which he had six years in a row, he didn't go beyond the fifth grade. He had known terrible poverty, too. Until he was a young man, he had never owned any underwear or even a necktie. He wore rough, hand-sewn breeches, a homemade hickory shirt, and a coat made of coarse cotton cloth. He wore yarn socks that Ma or one of his sisters knitted for him.

Johnnie's mother knew how to take sheep's wool, wash it, card it, and make it into homemade yarn. She had a big loom in the kitchen on which she wove a strong, rough cloth called linsey-woolsey. She strung the loom with linen warp, then wove with wool—so the cloth had the strength of linen and the warmth of wool. The homespun cloth she made was usually brown, because butternuts and black walnuts were plentiful and easily obtained as a dye.

Whenever Johnnie cleaned the fireplace, he poured the ashes into a barrel Ma kept by the smokehouse. It stood on a platform, and had a hole at the bottom and a crock under the hole. Ma or someone poured a bucket of water into the barrel several times a week, and almost pure lye leached out of the ashes. Later the leached residue was put on the garden. Ma used this lye and pork grease to make strong yellow soap used for everything—clothes, baths, faces, hands, and scrub work.

Ella, one of Johnnie's sisters, married a man named Bill Jarrett, and they settled on a farm nearby. Ida married Andy Cottongin, who kept the general store in the nearby town of Tunket. Andy also had charge of the post office in one corner of his store.

Johnnie farmed for Ma, but he hated it. It was not farm work he hated as much as staying in one place so long. He'd never been out of Indiana. He hadn't gone far enough in school to study geography or history. But Ella had, and he used to take her geography book to the barn loft and study it hungrily, spelling the words aloud to himself. The middle spread of the old book had a map of the United States.

"I'm going to see this country with my own eyes," he promised himself. His lean finger traced the states—Wyoming, Idaho, Colorado, North Dakota, and South Dakota. Ella's book said that region was the breadbasket of the world.

"I'll see wheat fields—miles long—like it says here," he mused happily, looking off into the cobwebbed corners of the old barn. They seemed to stretch out in his imagination to the ripples and dips and sweeps of yellow grain fields he'd never seen.

One night Johnnie walked by the church. Music was being played, and he could hear people singing inside. Finally, when no one was looking, he sneaked into one of the back seats and sat down.

Because the place was lighted by hanging lamps, the light was often uncertain and people's faces were in half darkness. That night a visiting preacher spoke.

Usually old Brother Bellows would be there thunderously shaking a "brimstone wallet" in the faces of the trembling people. He usually gave himself to the evident pleasure of describing hell with all its pain and terror. "The odor of brimstone is on your very garments," he would thunder, his eyes flashing. "You're on the very brink of perdition. The flames are leaping into your very faces!" And the people would cover their eyes and moan aloud with fear of the wrath to come.

But tonight a man stood up there talking—not shouting. His face was calm, kind, and good. He talked about Jesus Christ, and made Him seem real to Johnnie. He could almost picture Christ walking along roads like those around home. Johnnie thought, "If I knew a fellow like that, I'd follow Him everywhere." The church was still. A few June bugs bumbled about the hot lamp chimneys. But the kind voice of the minister went on and on. Finally, because Johnnie was weak from his last sickness, he couldn't control his emotions, and he began to cry a little noisily. People looked at him curiously. This made him so ashamed that he got up and stumbled out into the night, wiping his eyes and blowing his nose on his ragged red handkerchief. His heart had not been this touched since he was a small boy and had heard someone read the Christmas story aloud.

Under the stars in the cool evening air he began to

think more clearly as he walked home. The gravel crunched under his rough farm shoes. The spell of the kindly minister was still upon him. "I'll be a Christian when I get to be twenty-one," he promised himself.

Johnnie began to realize that night that even a little education had advantages. He realized also that he had wasted his life and had not studied in school when he had the chance. Now it was almost too late. Maybe people in town would think he was somebody if he ran away from home. Then he would come back and show them all a thing or two. He'd go—that's what he'd do, as soon as harvest was over. In October he would leave—October, or in the spring.

CHAPTER SEVEN

Leaving Home

JOHNNIE was tall, lanky, and ignorant. He could hardly read a paragraph in Ella's school reader. His family had been poor, hardworking, and respectable; but everything he had tried to accomplish in life seemed a failure, such as the time he decided to raise chickens. He worked for a week preparing a good hen house and a chicken run. Ma gave him two old hens and some eggs. But nearly all of the baby chicks turned out to be roosters, and he hadn't even made three dollars after all his hard work. He'd tried to hire out, but there just didn't seem to be any place to find work. Money was scarce. Besides, nearly all the farm families around had half-grown sons who worked.

Johnnie liked geography in school. He looked at Ella's big geography book by the hour. He had his own state—Indiana—spotted on the map. He knew its shape and could point out the big cities in it. He had often asked his sister to read to him when she wasn't busy helping Ma.

"What's that, Ella?" he'd ask, pointing to a patch on the map, north of Indiana and greenish in color.

4

"Why, that's Michigan, Johnnie. Named for the big lake west of it, I reckon. And there's another lake on the east, too."

"Read what it says, Ella."

"Johnnie, you oughta try to read yourself. You're a terrible big boy to be so dumb. The more you read, the easier it'll get. I can't help you, reading *to* you."

"Well, read it now, anyhow," he begged. "I can't get much spellin' out words, like I have to."

"It says, 'Mildly rolling, rich soil, protected from westerly winds by Lake Michigan. Particularly adapted to small fruits and orchards.' It says the soil is good."

"Does it say anything about wheat? Where are the big wheat fields, miles and miles long, I've heard about?"

Ella looked at Johnnie closely. She was suspicious of him.

"Why do you want to know that, Johnnie?" She was wary of his wanting to know so much.

If Johnnie wasn't careful, she might tell Ma, and Ma had gimlet eyes that bored into you.

"Aw, I just like to hear about those great big fields. Sounds so wonderful." He tried to talk as if he were only interested in reading about things. Ella was off her guard again.

"Well, there are mighty big wheat fields in Kansas and Iowa. But that's far away from here. Hundreds and hundreds of miles. And cold, too. I've heard it gets fifty below zero."

"I wonder if they have big threshing machines, and big reapers, and riding plows," he said, his eyes looking off at nothing, not seeing Ma's dish cupboard, or the kitchen pump, or the stove. He seemed to see the fields, wide and yellow—and men working like so many beetles under a blazing harvest sun. That's where he wanted to be before a year was up.

Ella shut the book. "Of course," she said. "They do things in a big way out there. Why, I've heard that literally hundreds and hundreds of men make their living following the harvest."

"What's 'following the harvest,' Ella?"

"Oh—I think it's single fellows, who want adventure, or who can't find work at home, who go where work is plentiful, I s'pose. But don't bother me. Ma needs me. She's making soap. And you got chores to do, too, remember."

She started off toward the stove, where soup was bubbling up. She took off the lid and began stirring.

"Don't *you* get any idees," she said severely. "You know Ma needs you. She couldn't do without you."

But Johnnie thought she could. Ben Cotherin, who had lost his wife two years before, had been coming regularly to see Ma. She was pretty, in a slim, lively way; and her hair was only lightly streaked with gray. When she combed her hair, parted it in the middle, and looped it down over each ear, she looked young. When she wore her percale dress with white leaves and red rosebuds, even Johnnie, with the critical eyes of youth, could see why Ben came two or three times a week.

He often came in time for supper, and it was plain that Ma went to a little extra effort. She always used a fresh, smoothly ironed tablecloth and the best dishes.

Ben brought things, too—things even Johnnie looked forward to. Once he even brought a whole keg of chocolate drops with pink and white centers. For once, Johnnie's sweet tooth was satisfied.

Ben brought a big basket of apricots one day, picked from his own trees. Everyone knew Ben Cotherin had a good farm. His stock was better than that of most farmers in the county. Ben and Ma would make a good couple, Johnnie assured himself.

"I'll leave on Wednesday," he decided. "Ma and Ella will have my clothes all washed and ironed by then. I'll be real careful—I'll not get dirty if I can help it."

On Tuesday, Ma was in the washhouse cutting up potatoes to plant, and Tenny was working at a neighbor's. Johnnie climbed to the attic for an old traveling case called a "telescope bag" Pa had used. He began to pack his things, hiding the telescope bag behind the bed in the far corner. Each time Ella brought in a shirt or a handkerchief, he folded it bunglingly and put it in the bag.

Johnnie did not once think of the sorrow and anxiety he would cause when he ran away from home. All he could think of were the waving wheat fields and of earning money he could spend just as he pleased.

"I'm going to buy big cigars at the store when I get my own money," he boasted to himself, as if that were an ambition to look forward to.

"I'll have a ring on my finger and a watch in my pants pocket," he determined. "And if I want to, I'll just walk into a saloon and buy a drink of beer. And I'll get a fine tobacco pipe, too." Johnnie finished packing.

Early the next morning he dressed quietly and carried the telescope bag outside and hid it between the fence and the lilac bush. Then he did his chores for the last time. He milked the three cows and carried the milk in and set it on the table in the screened porch. Ma was already up. He could see the lamplight shining on the bushes by her bedroom window. His conscience troubled him a little. He knew his going away without telling anyone would grieve Ma. It did not occur to him to write a note, for spelling and writing were hard for him.

He went to the cupboard and got out a big chunk of corn bread. Pouring milk into a tall glass, he savored the cream that clung thickly on the top.

Then he saw that the lamp was moving from Ma's bedroom to the kitchen. He must go or be caught by Ma, whose keen eyes could look through a fellow. He gave one look around—a long look, for already he was realizing a little that he was taking a big step. From now on, he would have to dig for what he got. Food came easy here at Ma's house—regularly, three times a day. By noon where would he be eating? He got a big chunk of corn bread and put it in his pocket, picked up four or five apples, and slipped quietly out. He picked up his bag and ran down the dark country road. Day was already streaking the east. It was almost time for the five o'clock train to clatter through the little town. It always slowed down to throw off the mail, and that would give him his chance for free transportation. Johnnie had four dollars in his pocket.

CHAPTER EIGHT

The Train Ride

THE YEAR Johnnie ran away from home, Grover Cleveland was President of the United States. A sleepy atmosphere lay over the whole world. Some men were dreaming and pondering daringly how to change everything in the world. That early morning, rainbows shone on the tangled spider webs on the dew-flecked grass, but Johnnie didn't see them. Blithely he kicked up the dust of the road and whistled a gay tune. The early morning sun was warm on his back, for he was headed west, in both his dreams and in reality.

He had wanted to get away from Spartaville for a long time. People had always said, "That's Johnnie Lee. He hasn't got through the fifth grade. He's dumb as a goat."

"I'm not dumb," Johnnie said aloud to himself. "I never will have a chance in Spartaville."

Then in the distance he heard the whistle of the train. He began to walk a little faster and reached the depot as the train was slowing down. Johnnie glanced around to see that no railroad personnel was watching him. None was in sight. He seized the railing at the side of a boxcar and, scrambling quickly, was inside and out of sight in an instant. He huddled in the corner, settled down as comfortably as he could, with his old straw suitcase propped up beside him. The train picked up speed, and the cars began swaying from side to side. Johnnie was sure the car he was riding in would jerk loose from the others and catapult violently down the steep grade.

"I'll be killed, and they'll bury me, and Ma'll never know where her Johnnie went," he whimpered. Two tears glistened on his cheeks as he hung onto the side of the car so hard his knuckles turned white.

Then the train went over a bridge, so high that the houses looked like cardboard boxes in the valley below. A team of horses crossing a plowed field seemed no larger than black ants hitched to a pillbox.

Soon he became used to the jolting and swaying. He cautiously looked out and saw the name of a station, and this filled him with excitement. "Why, I remember this place!" he said aloud. "It's on the map, and not far from the Illinois line."

He ate his corn bread; then he wanted a drink. A dipperful of water from the pump by Ma's back door would taste better than anything. Remembering his apples, he ate all five, even the cores. It helped somewhat, but he was still thirsty, and hungry enough to eat a whole loaf of Ma's bread.

He had no watch, but by looking at the sun, he thought it must be about noon. He knew his mother would be putting food on the dinner table about now. She'd have a big skillet of fried cabbage and a pot of boiled potatoes, with thick cream and butter. He'd seen Ma's cheese bag draining the evening before. That meant fresh cottage cheese glistening with yellow cream. He was so hungry that he walked up and down the narrow boxcar. Later he tried to sleep. After walking some more, he still could think of nothing but food.

About midafternoon, the train began to slow down again, and he prepared to jump off when he could. He saw a water tank ahead, and knew the train would come to a complete stop to take on water, so he wouldn't have to jump off and get skinned and bruised.

He left the train and went down the steep embankment, slipping, almost falling down several times. He climbed a rail fence and followed a narrow, dusty country road. A fine red barn was on his left about half a mile down the rutted road. A white farmhouse stood beyond it, fairly advertising industry. Brightening with hope, he walked briskly toward the big, well-fenced farm. Sleek cattle grazed in green pastures. Streams of clear water cut through the well-tended fields.

He noted with pleasure that the fence around the large house was painted a gleaming white. Everything looked prosperous. He asked a little boy shooting at birds with a slingshot the name of the nearest town. The boy's trouser legs were torn, and a ragged straw hat covered his face. "It's Cullyville," he answered. " 'Tain't big, but it has a store an' a post office an' a depot."

Johnnie entered the lane leading to the farmhouse and walked toward a big well-kept barn. A man came out of the barn. He seemed important and businesslike, and Johnnie concluded he must be the owner.

"Were you looking for someone?" the man asked.

"Why—uh—yes, sir, I'm looking for work. I lived over in Indiana. My Pa died, and I need to earn my own living."

"Can you work?" The man's sharp eyes seemed to bore Johnnie's gangling form through and through.

"I've worked all my life," Johnnie declared. "After my Pa died, I helped Ma until she got married again. Then my stepfather and I ran the farm. He's gone now, and Ma's got her pension, and it keeps her going real good."

"I can use you. Go put your suitcase in that workers' house. There's a spare bed. You eat at the house. Had any dinner?"

"No, sir, I ain't; and my stomach has been arguing with me for an hour."

The man grinned. "Well, you go on to the kitchen. We got through eating a while ago, but Nellie'll fix you up. She's the hired girl. Then come to the barn. Nels or I will give you something to do."

Johnnie washed his hands with pump water and wiped them dry on a clean linen roller towel and was soon sitting down before a bountiful meal. Nellie brought in dumplings, roasted potatoes, pudding, a plate of roast meat, and big slices of homemade bread.

"Young fellow, you must have a pair of hollow legs." Fat Nellie laughed when she cut a generous piece of pie and filled his milk glass three times.

"I've been traveling," Johnnie said, joyful that he was at last doing what he had wanted to do for a long time. He had always wanted to travel.

"Come far?" asked middle-aged, inquisitive Nellie.

Nothing exciting had ever happened to her, and she was quite taken by other people's adventures. Her blue eyes peered at him through strong glasses.

"Since daylight," Johnnie answered. "On the train. Came from Indiana." He said it as if it had been Pakistan or Madagascar.

"Oh—you came in on the noon train!" she exclaimed. "That must be exciting. I ain't never rode on trains. Were you much afraid?"

It did Johnnie good to be the purveyor of information. Before, he had always sat and listened owl-eyed to stories of trips to Indianapolis, or even Richmond, Indiana. He had met only a few people who had gone as far as Chicago.

"Well, ma'am," he said, glad for an audience, "it was like riding on the wind. I saw ever so many fellows plowing in fields, and crows cawing and wind a-blowing the trees. Houses seemed to run by, and children yelled at the train going by so fast."

Johnnie had begun on his fat piece of new apple pie. Nellie had given him a piece of mild cheese, which he placed neatly on top of the pie.

"Cup o' coffee?" Nellie asked, reaching for the big granite coffee pot; but Johnnie shook his head.

"I ain't never been weaned," he declined laughingly, reaching out his empty glass. "I'll drink milk and be able to make out a good afternoon of work."

CHAPTER NINE

The Mitchell Farm

THE FARM was owned by a family named Mitchell. Johnnie proudly surveyed what he thought must be the most prosperous farm in that part of Illinois. The fences were in order, the stock was of the best, the barns were kept in good repair, and the house and yard were neat. He didn't see a single dilapidated shed or an unpainted building on the property. He was happy to belong to such an establishment.

"It's a good deal better'n Greg's farm," he mused. "And the Mitchells work hard, all of them. Old Greg never did a lick of work. He would have known how the rest of us live, if he had."

Johnnie helped with the horses, around the barn, and with the chores. His stepfather had taught him how to keep a barn clean, so he did a thorough job in the stalls and barnyard.

Mr. Mitchell was pleased and said so. "You work like someone taught you how to do it the right way," he commented, and it warmed Johnnie's heart.

Johnnie was not used to praise. Ma was good, but she had not praised her children much. "You ought to do good work because it is the right thing to do," she had said, and Johnnie had often wished she would tell him when his work had been particularly well done.

Johnnie was promised twenty-five dollars a month plus room and board and washing, and if he had owned a horse, its keep would have been included, also. The hired men lived in a bunkhouse which had once been the home of Mr. Mitchell's parents. There were beds, dressers, and chairs for the men. It was heated by a hard-coal base burner, which glowed and kept the rooms comfortable all night. A hired girl, Nellie's older sister, Sophia, came in every morning and made up the beds, swept, and mopped the floor. She was tall and wore steel-rimmed spectacles. She seldom said a word, but she did her work well, winning the appreciation of the hardworking farmhands.

"It's perty good to come back to a nice clean bed every night," Nels Hanson observed to Johnnie. "Old Mitchell, he takes right good care of his help, and they stay, too. I've been here ever since his Pa ran the farm. Every Saturday our clean clothes are put right in our own dresser drawers. That Sophia, she don't make a mistake. No monkey business here. I worked once where the men had to stay in a place not fit for hogs."

When Johnnie got his first pay, Mr. Mitchell took him aside. "Better put most of it in the bank, son," he advised kindly. "You will need it by and by, but not only that—it might come up missing. We have had some sticky fingers around the bunkhouse."

Johnnie appreciated the fatherly counsel. That day he rode to the village and opened an account in the local bank. He deposited twenty-three dollars, keeping only two for pocket money. He bought a little sack of stick candy. He had seldom had any candy at Ma's house, and it did his soul good to have a little something to chew on once in a while. He bought enough to have a stick a day until he got his pay again.

After supper the men sat around in what used to be the homestead kitchen. Sophia always had wood in the stove on cool evenings so that the men needed only to light it with a match. A brown granite coffeepot sat on the stove to fill up their mugs if the men wanted to drink coffee. Johnnie thought he was having the time of his life, smoking with the men, playing cards at the kitchen table, or swapping yarns.

The quickest way to lose a job with Mr. Mitchell was to appear a little tipsy on the job. Mr. Mitchell's words cut like a knife on such occasions. "Out of here!" he would say sharply, his eyes snapping fire. "I will have no liquor here, now or ever. I have children, sons and daughters. I don't want such sights as you are around, and I don't want liquor swillers around my stock and my barns, either."

He had a hard-and-fast rule against smoking around the barns, too. Johnnie had heard him fire a couple of men, one for smoking in the barn and the other for getting drunk on a Saturday night.

It was really a pleasure for Johnnie to see his bank account grow. By August he had sixty-two dollars in the bank, a new pair of work shoes, a pair of pants, and some real underwear, the first store-bought underwear he had ever owned. It was made of knit balbriggan, which felt much better than the coarse underwear Ma made of heavy flour sacks for him. The men had laughed when they saw the black letters "Crosby's Best Flour" stamped on the seat of his old undershorts.

Now he felt like one of the men, with good things to wear. When he went to church, sometimes he looked at the girls. Sometimes they glanced back at him.

In two years he had a horse—not the best, but good enough. He also bought a secondhand buggy, which he kept neat. He had clothes in his dresser and some money in the bank.

Once in a while Johnnie wondered about Ma, Ella, Tenny, and Ida. Sometimes at night he became a little homesick, but not often. He would somehow soothe his conscience. "She's got her pension. She won't lack for food and clothing as long as Uncle Sam keeps paying her," Johnnie reasoned.

Sometimes he worried that she might die while he was gone, and he thought how sorry he would be to return home to see her grave, instead of her, alive and well. He could hardly bear such thoughts.

But then, he would remember his pretty horse, Dexter, munching oats in his stall, and his buggy painted black, with bright yellow wheels. He would think about his money in the bank.

He would also think about Melinda, the girl he had taken out riding a few times. Such thoughts comforted him, and he would go to sleep again.

CHAPTER TEN

Melinda

FOR THE FIRST TIME Johnnie had a girl friend he really liked. Melinda Waters lived on the farm next to the Mitchell place. Her parents were frugal and prosperous in a rather cautious way. They hardly doled out a penny for anything not actively and urgently needed. People laughed at them, and this was hard on the teen-age children, Melinda and Marta. Naturally they longed for pretty things, nice clothes, and a decent place where they could invite their friends.

The floors of their house had no carpets; the dishes were cracked and old. The girls had to wear their clothes until they were ashamed to appear in public in them. As soon as the girls became eighteen, they both got jobs with neighbors. The entire neighborhood became incensed when Jake Waters tried to persuade the girls to give him their wages to "save" for them. Melinda told Johnnie about it.

"I'm not going to let him have a cent!" she cried in wrath. "I know how he would save it! He would put it in the bank in his name and that would be the last I would see of it."

She was cleaning the Mitchell kitchen following the noon meal. Johnnie said nothing as he watched her, but he thought how pretty she looked.

"This is the first time in my life I have ever had a pretty dress. I even like to work in pretty dresses. I can work better. Pa used to get us old dresses out of grandma's trunk and make us wear them."

She turned and faced Johnnie. "I am not going to wear an ugly dress again if I can help it!" she exclaimed.

She was in a pink calico dress, with a wide tucked and ruffled skirt. It was too good for every day, Johnnie thought. Her dark hair curled around her lovely face, and Johnnie was flattered that she talked to him. He looked all right now, he knew. He didn't have cutdown pants made from some of Pa's. He knew too well what it meant to be made fun of, so he saw in Melinda a person who had suffered as he had. Greg had made his school days miserable by making fun of his clothes.

"That's a pretty dress you're wearing," he ventured shyly. "It looks like a flower garden, with you in the middle of it."

"Why, thank you, Johnnie," Melinda said, her lips curving in a smile. "That was a pretty speech, and it was a lovely compliment, too."

"Isn't it lucky you stay at the Mitchells'? If you lived at home, your Pa would pester you all the time for your money, and he might make you pay board," Johnnie said.

"That is just what he would do," Melinda agreed, her eyes beginning to snap again. "But you know, Johnnie, I do feel sorry for Ma. She never gets a piece of candy or a single new thing. I'm going to buy a piece of pretty goods and make her a new dress. She misses us girls terribly."

"I'd think she would," Johnnie agreed. "Say, would you like for me to take you over one of these days in my buggy? Dexter needs a little more running. He's getting too fat. We could go in the evening or on Sunday."

"Why, Johnnie, that would be wonderful!" She sparkled. "I have a little time every afternoon, and Mrs. Mitchell lets me use her sewing machine. I can make the dress by Thursday night. Thursday is her birthday. Let's go Thursday night."

"I'll get her a sack of candy when we go through town," Johnnie promised. "I'll get a sack for us, too. That will be fun."

"Oh, Johnnie, you are so good!" Melinda cried, and Johnnie lingered a little longer, enjoying her enthusiasm.

Life began to mean more to Johnnie than the enjoyment of his pipe, his horse, and his bank account. He had a buggy ride to look forward to. He washed it on Wednesday night, and after supper on Thursday he put on his best clothes and picked up Melinda.

Melinda, starched and fluffy, was ready when he drove to the side gate. She tripped out, with her mother's dress wrapped carefully in a newspaper. Johnnie bought a sack of bright-colored gumdrops and one of bright-colored hard candy for Melinda's mother, and another sack of mixed candy they could eat while riding.

Johnnie was happier than he had ever been before.

He began to save feverishly. Now he had $111.50 in the bank, even after buying the buggy and horse.

There were times when Mr. Mitchell took Johnnie into Salemfore when he had business to transact, and Johnnie found himself looking at bureaus, dining tables, and parlor furniture. He was eager to make more money and began to wonder if he shouldn't look for work which paid more than Mr. Mitchell did. But he gave that idea up, realizing that he was already getting top wages.

He bought little presents for Melinda—a pretty brooch, some ribbon, a bracelet, a locket. He was happy to see her wearing them, though he hated to spare the money.

Johnnie began looking for a nice Christmas present for Melinda. He was going to draw some of his money from the bank and get a set of the dishes she liked so well. They were prettier than any he had ever seen—and cost a pretty price, too. But Johnnie didn't feel too bad about that. It would be a start toward their own household; they would probably still be using them when they celebrated their golden wedding anniversary. He laughed at that thought, since the time seemed so far away.

When Johnnie went to draw some money out of the bank, Mr. Mitchell followed him in and laid a hand on his arm.

"What are you going to do, Johnnie?" he asked kindly.

"I am going to buy Melinda a set of dishes she has set her heart on," he said proudly. "I want her to have them for Christmas." Then he laughed. "Could be, I'll be eating off them myself," he added with deep pleasure.

But Mr. Mitchell did not smile.

A warning bell rang in Johnnie's heart. "Why, what's the matter, Mr. Mitchell?" he asked, his lips stiff with fear and foreboding.

"Johnnie, don't you let on that I told you, but that Melinda is no good. She has been two-timing you for six months now. You know she says she is going to see her mother every Wednesday and Sunday night? Well, you just drive over there and hide in the alder thicket, and you'll see. You know Ben Peters? Works for the Akers? She meets him right there at her Ma's house."

Johnnie could only look at his employer in dumb misery. The light had gone out of his life.

"I thought you would catch on. She's been laughing at you behind your back for giving her things for her and Ben. You are worth two of Ben Peters. I won't have him working for me. He drinks, and he smokes all the time. I don't want my animals abused or my barns burned. He's one of the worst men in the neighborhood."

"But she has been taking from me, fairly asking for stuff!" protested Johnnie. He could hardly believe such deceitfulness was possible. He was sure, though, that Mr. Mitchell would not lie to him.

"What has made me boil," Mr. Mitchell continued, "is that I heard them making fun of you only last night. I heard Ben say, 'Go it, Lindy; get all you can outa the old sucker. It'll save us buyin' the stuff. Maybe we can make our weddin' trip outa what he saves us!'"

Johnnie felt that his legs would give way under him.

"Mr. Mitchell," he said stiffly, "I can't work for you anymore. I can't face the fellows—face her. I like working for you, but I can't stay on now. I just can't."

Mr. Mitchell nodded sympathetically. "I hate to lose you, Johnnie—you're one of my most dependable hands —but I don't blame you. I'll tell you what. Why don't you just take off a couple or three months and drive home and see your Ma? Take her a nice present, Johnnie. She is more worthy than Melinda. You come back next March. Your job will be here waiting for you when you want to come back."

"I'll get my stuff out of the bunkhouse while the men are in the barn. I won't say good-bye to anyone."

"Good idea," said Mr. Mitchell. "But I do want to say the men will be glad you have caught onto that Melinda. They were all sore. It'll do the whole bunch of them good to see Melinda's game spoiled. There ain't a one there who would have her. They don't like dirty work any more than I do."

No one was in the bunkhouse when Johnnie went in, folded his nice clothes, put them in his suitcase, and covered it with his extra lap robe in the buggy. Then he drove down the barn lane so that he wouldn't go near the house. While packing, he had seen Melinda on the back porch looking in his direction and waving her hand, but he ignored her.

Johnnie drove all night, arriving in the morning at a small town, where he stabled his horse and found a restaurant. He ate a big breakfast, then talked to the livery man, who let him sleep on a cot in his office until noon. It was chilly outside, but no snow was on the ground. He ate dinner in the same restaurant, and in the afternoon he drove on. For supper he stopped at a place which advertised, "Home Cooking." "Nothing like Ma's home cooking," he told himself, chewing a tough biscuit and looking with disfavor at the soggy potatoes. "Ma never set anyone down to such a meal as this."

He bought corn and oats for his horse, then continued his trip. At the end of the third day, almost exhausted, he came to the outskirts of his own hometown. He perked up as he realized how close home was now, and his weariness seemed to leave him. He had lost to some extent his disappointment over Melinda, for his sorrow had been mingled with outrage at the way she had used him.

He could hardly wait to get home now. He had presents for each of his sisters and a tall glass pitcher and six pretty glasses for Ma, who had never owned anything so nice.

As he entered the outskirts of his hometown, it pleased him to identify the places he had known so well but had not seen for a long time. There was Hector's Barber Shop, with someone in the chair getting a haircut. Nearby was Giles' Blacksmith Shop and Haynes' General Store.

CHAPTER ELEVEN

A Visit Home

HE DROVE through town to Ma's familiar yard, noting the firm, beautiful way the wood had been nailed to the sides of the house. He remembered the sawdust his father had packed between the walls to keep the house warm in the winter and cool in the summer.

The trees in the yard were a little taller, the bush by the porch was higher—he had planted that bush which old Granny Hawkins had given him.

The door opened, and Ma looked out with curiosity to see who was driving into her yard. Then, for a moment, the two looked at each other until recognition and unbelief showed on Ma's face. She flung the door open and ran across the porch and down the steps, disregarding the cold air.

"Johnnie, Johnnie!" she cried, tears streaming down her cheeks. "Johnnie, Johnnie, where have you been, Johnnie; and why didn't you let us know? Why did you go away and leave your Ma, Johnnie? I loved you so. I mourned you; I mourned you; I almost died—I—I——"

Johnnie jumped from his buggy and in a trice was

holding his mother, kissing her wet cheeks. He was weeping, too.

"I didn't mean to leave you like that, Ma," he said, his voice breaking. "Honest I didn't, Ma. I didn't know you cared that much. You know I ain't no hand to write, and can't do it very well, anyhow."

"But, Johnnie, suppose something had happened—suppose you had got sick or been killed—how would I have known?"

"I know, Ma, it wasn't right; but I had to get out of this town. The boys pestered me about my clothes, and I was failing in school. I couldn't get work here. No chance for a fellow here. But I'm back, Ma, and I aim to stay till spring, anyway."

She led him into the house and plied him with questions and gave him all the food he could hold. He learned that Tenny had also married and lived nearby. Ma was alone. She had rented her farm, and her sons-in-law helped with her garden.

Johnnie settled down in his old home happily and comfortably. Now when he went into town, no one laughed at him. Even Greg looked at him with respect, for Johnnie wore his new clothes. This gave Johnnie a sense of importance he had never felt before.

He did Ma's outside work, cleaning the barn and the hen house, mending the roof and the storm door, and putting a new board in the porch floor, where it had started to rot.

"Oh, it is so good to have you home, Johnnie," Ma said again and again. Johnnie looked at her uneasily, for he did not plan to stay long.

Johnnie had tasted freedom. Having learned to command respect and having discovered the pleasure of earning his own money, he knew he could not stay on the farm. Ma could not afford to pay him, and she could not afford on her small pension to buy him the things he needed.

"I aim to stay until March, Ma," he told her firmly. "I can't stay beyond that. Mr. Mitchell is expecting me to come back then. I have to help get the fields ready for planting, and the livestock will need more care. He will need me to repair the barns and the fences."

"But, Johnnie, I need you here. I need you terribly," she told him.

"No, you don't, Ma. You couldn't pay me what I need, and I need money. I am a man, Ma, and I can't work for nothing; and the girls' husbands help you. I'll get things all mended and fixed up before I leave. I have to earn my own way, Ma."

His mother knew this was true, but she pleaded just the same. But no amount of cajoling could make him stay when March finally came. He promised to write to her this time.

Early on a cold, blustery morning in March, Johnnie left. He was ashamed to realize that he was as eager to get away as he had been to get home last December. He felt the urge to earn money, to get more clothes, for the winter had been hard on his work clothes. He wanted to see his bank account grow and to get settled again.

When he drove into the lane of the Mitchell farm at noon on the fourth day, he sensed that something was wrong.

He learned the bad news from one of the hands who came out of the barn to greet him. Mr. Mitchell had died shortly after Christmas. Kicked in the face by a new horse he bought at an auction, he contracted blood poisoning and died in three days. Johnnie was invited to eat in the kitchen. Mrs. Mitchell came in. Her eyes filled with tears as she talked with Johnnie.

"He liked you so much, Johnnie," she said, her voice breaking. "He and I both felt bad about the way Melinda used you."

"I will always be glad for his advice," Johnnie said simply, after offering his deepest sympathy.

"Well, as the old saying goes, 'she took her pigs to a poor market.' She married Ben at Christmastime and has rued the day ever since then, they tell me. He drinks like a fish, and was turned off from where he worked. He is running through all the money she saved! She should have married you, Johnnie—or stayed with her folks, sorry as they are!"

The next day Johnnie drew his money from the bank and headed west. He did not know where he was going, but he determined to try his luck again, as he had at the first. He drove all afternoon. At nightfall he stopped at a small hotel in a little railroad town. His horse was cared for in a big barn in connection with the hostelry. The next morning after breakfast, he asked the clerk if anyone in the area needed a good farmhand.

The clerk laughed. "All the farmers around here need good hands," he answered. "But I will tell you of a really good place. You drive down the hard road west, and you'll see a big white house and a red barn on the left about four miles out. That will be the Babcocks. The biggest landowners around here, with a lot of stock, they are nearly always needing help. They are pretty good folks to work for, too."

Johnnie drove toward the Babcock farm, wondering if he would like it as well as he had at the Mitchells'. He looked interestedly at the countryside and at the setting sun. "It seems I'm going west all the time," he said to no one in particular. He was pleased. "Maybe that's what I'll just keep doing. I'd like to see Iowa, and Nebraska, and Colorado, and the mountains. I've never seen a mountain in all my life."

The Babcocks hired Johnnie. They were pleased with the recommendation Mrs. Mitchell had written for him. He carried his belongings to a long bunkhouse built by the west pasture fence. A pump stood in front of it.

A hired girl cleaned the bunkhouse two or three times a week. She did a thorough job, but the place was not as pleasant as at the Mitchells'. There was a special dining room for the hired hands off the big kitchen. The men seldom saw any of the Babcocks. A general manager took care of the farm. He was a curt, unfriendly fellow who seldom spoke to anyone except to give orders.

"I feel like a slave instead of a farmhand," Johnnie remarked to one of the men one day when they were washing at a bench outside the kitchen door. "It ain't friendly like the other place I worked. Mr. Mitchell always took an interest in all of us, and we had a better place to stay. We had better food, too."

"Good pay here, though," the other answered indifferently. "I guess I can stand it for the money I send home to my wife and children. Couldn't get any work back home."

"Where is your home?" Johnnie asked curiously, glad in a way he did not have a wife to worry about or to divide his money with.

"Arkansas," replied the man, with a touch of pride in his voice. "It's a mighty pretty place to live, but us hill folks are poor. I live on as pretty a hilltop as you could ever see, but the only people I know who make any money there make moonshine."

CHAPTER TWELVE

Westward to Colorado

JOHNNIE WORKED two years for the Babcocks, saving every penny he could. He went home to see Ma and his sisters once during this time, staying a few months, but returning to the West he loved. Finally he hopped a freight train and ended up in Grand Junction, Colorado.

Ah, here was the place he'd dreamed about—mountains that were full of gold and silver ore. "I'd sure like to find a gold nugget to hang on my watch fob," Johnnie thought. "Wouldn't old Greg's eyes bug out?"

For several years Johnnie worked at various jobs. He washed dishes, worked at a restaurant, and even did some mining. In fact, he worked for two years in the mine. One day, working alone in a shaft, a sudden fear overwhelmed him. Even the palms of his hands began to cramp. Feeling that some terrible danger hung over him, he felt a wild impulse to flee. As he turned and ran, the roof of the mine fell in behind him. Where he had been standing, tons of rock and debris now lay.

"Lord," he whispered, "was it You who warned me just then? Lord, I'll try to do better."

Johnnie knew his life was not in accord with God's will. He was past the age of thirty-five. Often he remembered his promise to God that he would become a Christian at the age of twenty-one, and it hurt him to know that his promise was not being kept.

Johnnie quit the mine. His narrow escape from death unnerved him. Winter was coming on. Someone told him about a claim he could get at a cheap price in the mountains. Trapping was paying well, even better than mining. Johnnie decided to try it. The claim shanty was weathertight and comfortable in the mountain climate. There was a big fireplace, built-in bunk beds, and a sound board floor.

With his savings Johnnie bought traps, a grubstake, a new pair of boots, socks, a warm mackinaw, shirts, and pants. He moved into the cabin and worked hard repairing it and cutting enough wood for his fireplace and cookstove.

He made shelves for his provisions and devised hanging shelves to keep his food away from the pack rats. Then he set out a trapline, which kept him busy until noon every day.

CHAPTER THIRTEEN

Cabin in the Mountains

THE SNOW SOON CAME, and the wind howled around the lonely cabin high in the Colorado mountains. Johnnie found some timber piled near his cabin. He went to the town and bought a saw, some nails, and a carpenter's square.

He built a shed next to the door so that he could get wood without having to put on his coat and boots. The shed was tight and roomy, and it was a good place to store his pelts. From the ceiling he hung his meat.

Johnnie bought a geography book, and on some afternoons he eagerly pored over it, spelling out the words. He looked longingly at the maps, tracing other states farther west—Idaho, Oregon, Washington.

"Wish I could see 'em all," he whispered, a wistful look in his blue eyes. "I'm going to save. I'm going to see Washington and Oregon. I want to see the Snake River and the Columbia."

He tramped through the woods following his trapline, enjoying the cold, brisk air. Winter settled down, and snow lay in drifts everywhere; but Johnnie was snug in his cabin.

Johnnie was a neat housekeeper. He learned that from Ma. No dirty dishes were ever left lying on his table. He always put the "vittles" away, as Ma used to call the left-over food.

"It's pure laziness, leaving the table full of clutter," she used to say vehemently. So Johnnie always put a dishpan of water on the fire while he ate. He kept the windows clean, too. A woman in town did his washing and ironing for a small sum of money.

Johnnie's heap of pelts grew, and he looked forward to the money he would make when spring came.

"I'll get a job on a ranch in the spring," he decided. "I'll begin to save money again, like I did at Mitchell's. It felt good to have a little piece of money in the bank."

He washed up the dishes and cleaned the table. After sweeping the floor, he lit the lamp and set it up on the mantel. It was cold outside, and a sharp wind was blowing.

"I'm glad I'm not out in the cold tonight," he said, drawing his chair a little closer to the blazing fire. He usually let the fire in the cookstove go out, then he smoked and watched the fire until bedtime. But tonight he had just gotten settled when there was a loud banging on the shed door. He leaped to his feet.

CHAPTER FOURTEEN

The Man at the Door

AT FIRST a feeling of pleasure surged through Johnnie's heart, but that was soon replaced by one of fear. Was the caller a murderer, or a desperado escaped from the penitentiary? Or could it be a filthy tramp who had found his clean-swept cabin?

Johnnie laid his pipe on the mantel and put on his cap and mackinaw. He decided he would shut the house door and open the shed so that he could see who it was before he allowed anyone to come in for the night. He'd seen enough of the rough characters in the saloon to last for a lifetime. The banging continued. Johnnie lit a lantern.

He opened the shed door and saw by the dim light of the lantern a short, stocky man a little past middle age. The man's fur cap was pushed back; his face seemed pleasant and kind. A few clean locks of white hair showed from under his cap.

"Come in, stranger! Come in!" Johnnie said heartily, opening his house door.

The man entered quietly. Johnnie got another armload of wood for the fireplace.

"Just give me your coat, and sit here by the fire. I'll warm you a little supper," Johnnie told the stranger, who had not as yet had a chance to speak. He removed a clean overcoat and shook the snow from the shoulders. He took off his hat, and carefully set a case on the floor.

"My name is Pressbarger, David Pressbarger," he said, facing Johnnie. "I am a colporteur. I sell books."

"I like books," Johnnie said, smiling, putting the stranger's coat carefully on a wall peg near the fireplace. "Only I can't read too well. I like histories that tell of people in the olden days, and geography about far-off places."

"I do, too," said the man, seating himself by the fire, and holding out his hands to the warmth.

"I'll stir up the kitchen fire," Johnnie said, breaking kindling and stirring the dark-red coals. "I'll fix a big dish of soup beans. I'm sorry I run out of bacon and ham. I just flavored the beans with a hunk of butter. And I've got bread. I make my own sourdough. I hope you like it."

"I like butter-flavored beans well. My wife quit putting meat in them long ago," the pleasant visitor said.

Johnny felt happy. Soon a merry fire crackled. While the food cooked, Johnnie threw back the covers of the bed.

"You'll have to sleep with me, Mr. Pressbarger," he said. "I just got my clean things from Mrs. Posten yesterday, and I'll put clean sheets and blankets on the bed. I was going to tomorrow, but tonight is just as good."

6

Bread, butter, and hot beans tasted good to the weary colporteur, who had tramped many miles since daybreak. Johnnie opened a jar of apple butter and a can of peaches. This was the first guest in his house, and he wanted to make a real splurge.

"You really have fine bachelor quarters here, Mr.——"

"Lee," Johnnie said eagerly. "My name is Lee. Most people call me Johnnie. John Ed, my Ma named me thirty-six years ago."

When Johnnie had cleaned the dishes and pans, he sat beside the fire. To his amazement, he noted a strange thing. His guest was reading a Bible. The only people Johnnie ever associated with the Bible were preachers, and Johnnie didn't have a high opinion of those he knew. Some were lazy, sponging, sniveling, with only a Sunday brand of righteousness. One preacher from the Corinth church was a notorious drunk. And the Mount Pleasant preacher beat his wife and his horses. He knew few of them who had much real Christianity.

Johnnie took his fine meerschaum pipe from the mantelpiece and knocked out the ashes. Carefully he refilled it, lit up, and began to exhale puffs of smoke, smacking his lips appreciatively as he did so. He eyed the stranger curiously.

"Mr. Pressbarger," he said, removing his pipe from his mouth, "I take it you're a religious man, maybe a church member. I ain't, though I did promise God when I got to be twenty-one, I'd be a Christian."

His guest looked up, smiling. "Did you keep that promise, Johnnie?" he asked quietly.

CHAPTER SIXTEEN

Ready-made Family

MR. PRESSBARGER was gone when Johnnie returned from his trapline. The house seemed dark and lonely, and Johnnie couldn't understand this new feeling. He thought he was used to being alone. Then he remembered he hadn't used tobacco for three days.

"I didn't know I could do without it! I thought I had to be puffing or chewing," he exclaimed.

He found a Bible with a note beside it.

"Thank you for your kindness. I am leaving this Bible for you to study until you have time to buy one for yourself. I have another Bible at home."

Johnnie hunted three days before he found the Ten Commandments. The Bible had a concordance, but he didn't know how to use it. When he finally located the Ten Commandments, he learned them by heart.

In the spring Johnnie sold all his pelts and went to Longmont to work on a ranch. For the first time he asked to be off on Sabbath.

"Saturday, eh?" his prospective employer inquired. "Would you be willing to work on Sunday?"

"Oh, yes," Johnnie assured him, "I'll work every Sunday."

The next Sabbath he attended the Longmont Adventist Church where Mr. Pressbarger also attended. The colporteur asked Johnnie home for dinner. Johnnie stayed until sundown and was delighted at the way the family closed the Sabbath. He had never heard the songs they sang, such as "Day Is Dying in the West" and "Higher Ground." The Pressbargers gave him an old songbook, which he took home. All week he tried to sing the songs he had heard that first Sabbath. It was not long until he sang, and was able to quote Bible verses, all day. Then he was never lonely. His life was far different from what it had been a year before.

A few weeks later Johnnie joined the Longmont, Colorado, Seventh-day Adventist Church.

After his baptism Johnnie became a colporteur himself. For several years he worked in Nevada, Alaska, and Idaho. Often he walked, sometimes he rode horseback, selling hundreds of copies of *Bible Readings for the Home Circle*.

One winter when he was nearly forty years old, Johnnie went to church school with a dozen children not one fourth his age. He was embarrassed a bit, but his desire to learn to be a better reader was great. He stayed in school the full year.

Then he received a letter from Ma asking him to return home.

Johnnie was a different man from what he had been when he had left home many years before. He read newspapers, magazines, and books. He studied his Sabbath School lessons every day, and often taught classes.

When the train stopped at his hometown, he stepped off and looked about curiously. The town was smaller than he remembered it. He saw a few people whom he knew, but they glanced at him indifferently, then looked away. "They don't even know me!" Johnnie marveled. "Am I changed that much?"

He picked up his suitcase, hired a rig, and in a little while he was home. He unloaded the trunk and suitcase in the yard. For a moment he surveyed his old home. The door opened, and a thin, feeble woman walked out.

"Ma!" he cried. "It's me. It's Johnnie."

She began to cry, and Johnnie marveled at how tiny she was in his arms—so frail, so weak. It was hard to believe that it was Ma.

For four years Johnnie cared for Ma as tenderly as if she were a baby. She was too old to understand when he tried to explain religion to her. She didn't seem to miss the bacon he didn't cook with her eggs. Besides, she was just glad Johnnie was home.

Johnnie went to church every Sabbath in a nearby town. He was elected church elder and preached when the minister was away.

A widow who attended the same church caught Johnnie's eye, and he made friends with her. Soon they were seen often talking together. Minnie was a nurse with a married son and two grandsons. Johnnie proposed, and they were married. It was a good business transaction, for Johnnie got a ready-made family.

Minnie made home sweet and happy for Johnnie. He pruned fruit trees, set out berries, and planted big gardens. They worked together for three and a half years. Then Minnie died suddenly. For a while Johnnie lived alone working in his orchard and garden.

Letters came regularly from his stepson, who was a missionary in Africa. He loved to receive letters from Africa. Often he heard his stepgrandson preach in a church nearby. On Sunday he listened to the Voice of Prophecy broadcast on the radio and heard his other stepgrandson sing in a male quartet.

One day when he had a cash offer for his house, Johnnie made a sudden decision. "I'll take this money and go to Africa. I'll see my stepson. I'll see how the world looks on the other side of the globe."

And that is exactly what he did. Johnnie was in his middle sixties when he first walked onto the grounds of Malamulo Mission. He attended church even though he didn't understand a word that was said. He lived there awhile, made a garden, and set out orange, tangerine, and lemon trees. He grew peanuts, and canned dozens of jars of fruit for his stepdaughter-in-law. The African people loved him, for he was friendly and kind. In the truest sense he was a missionary, too.

Johnnie was ninety years old when he died. His sight had become so dim that he could no longer see to read his Bible. But the forty times he had read it through gave him a wonderful knowledge of the Word.

Even in the physical blindness of his old age, Johnnie often reflected on his conversion and the first time he had seen the light of the gospel. Four words Johnnie held in common with the revelator of the Bible: "And I John saw."